Christmas with Käthe Wohlfahrt

Christmas
with **Käthe**
Wohlfahrt

Christmas
with Käthe Wohlfahrt

1st Edition

© 1989 Käthe Wohlfahrt
No part of this book may be reproduced in any form without prior written permission from Käthe Wohlfahrt Christkindlmarkt.

Publisher:
Käthe Wohlfahrt Christkindlmarkt

Editor:
Harald Wohlfahrt

Text:
Elizabeth Linker, Ft. Worth, Texas

Design and Illustrations:
Elke Mader, Würzburg

Photography:
Fotostudio Drumm, Bad Windsheim
Werbestudio SG, Würzburg

also from:
Elmar Hahn Studios, Würzburg (P. 11, 12/13)
Bildarchiv Huber, Garm.-Partenkirchen (P. 16/17)
Jürgens Ost + Europa Photo, Köln (P. 22/23)
Edmund von König Verlag, Heidelberg (P. 21)
Mr. Oliver Rotzal (P. 72)

Decoration:
Käthe Wohlfahrt Christkindlmarkt
(Mrs. Gertrud Hornn and her team:
Mrs. Wuzel, Mrs. Kandert, and Miss Knorr)

Color Separations:
LT-Litho GmbH, Thüngen

Typesetter:
Formsatz GmbH, Würzburg

Printer:
Bonitas-Bauer, Würzburg

*Thanks to the kind assistance
and loans of artifacts from:*
Dr. Phil. Konrad Auerbach
(Museum of Erzgebirge Toys, Seiffen GDR)
Mr. Dettelbacher (Würzburg)
Irenco (Stockholm, Sweden), (P. 19)
Lebkuchen-Schmidt (Nürnberg)
Mrs. Monique Lindner (Rothenburg)
Dipl.-Ethn. Roland Schmidt
(Open Air Museum of Seiffen)
Toy Museum of Rothenburg o. d. Tauber
Mr. Trumpold (Göppingen)
and many others…

Special Thanks to:
Mr. and Mrs. Hanns Teichert
Mr. and Mrs. Dale Hanson,
and the "Christmas Family" in this book!

Käthe Wohlfahrt
D-8803 Rothenburg ob der Tauber
Herrngasse 2
Phone: 09861/409-0
Fax: 09861/40941

Table of Contents

Preface

Käthe and Wilhelm Wohlfahrt, founders of the Käthe Wohlfahrt Christkindlmarkt and Christmas Village.

Dear Friends!

Here in Rothenburg ob der Tauber, when fresh snow swirls round the towers and church spires and settles at last on the steep red roofs, when the sound of the first Christmas carol rings once more through the cobbled streets, the evening dark sends us hurrying homeward. The smell of evergreens fills the house, and the scent of gingerbread welcomes us home. It is time to bring out the Advent candles and prepare the house for the Christ Child's visit.

It is also time for questions and stories. When the Christmas box is brought down from the loft, the children in the Wohlfahrt family gather round Grandpa Wohlfahrt's chair and listen with wonder and delight as he tells them stories from the Erzgebirge, stories of angels and pyramids and the little church that the miners built. Down goes his hand into the box and out comes another story. Then the children ask him once again to explain about St. Nicholas, and the nutcrackers, and the Christmas tree, and Knight Rupert, and the smoking men. And, again and again he can be persuaded to answer just one more question.

This year, on the 25th Anniversary of the Käthe Wohlfahrt Company, our family would like to celebrate by sharing with you this special book, "Christmas with Käthe Wohlfahrt". It is filled with the history, traditions, and stories that mark the Christmas season and that make it a joyous time for our family. As you read the stories you may discover some delightful new traditions and customs, and from time to time, you may recognize an old familiar friend. We hope that this book will bring you much pleasure in the weeks and days leading up to Christmas and during the rest of the year as well. In the back of the book you will find an order form that includes many of the beautiful objects pictured in these pages.

We would like to thank all who made this book possible, those who provided pictures and texts, our son Harald whose idea it was, our daughters Birgit and Carmen, our daughter-in-law Humiko, our son-in-law Karl-Heinz, our grandchildren, Tanya, Simone, Aska Elisabeth, and Kenta Johannes, and of course you, the readers. In addition, we would like to extend a special invitation to you to visit our Christmas Village in Rothenburg ob der Tauber.

Wilhelm Wohlfahrt

Käthe Wohlfahrt

A Family Story

Although most of the stories in this book were first told many years ago, one is very recent indeed. With the help of the Wohlfahrt grandchildren, we would like to start by sharing with you a story which is very special to us – the story of Käthe Wohlfahrt's.

It begins in the Ore Mountains, or the Erzgebirge as we call them here, a beautiful region of forests and mountains that lies in Eastern Germany in an area once called Saxony, not far from the cities of Dresden and Leipzig.

Wilhelm Wohlfahrt – the children would like to explain that this is "Grandpa" – grew up in the little village of Stützengrün on his family's farm in the Erzgebirge and expected that he would always live there. Even after World War II, when the Soviets occupied the land, Wilhelm and his young wife, Käthe, lived and worked on their dairy farm. But the farm was now a collective, and Wilhelm and Käthe knew that the future held little promise for them. So carrying little with them but their memories and courage and hope, the couple boarded separate trains to attempt their escape to the West. With their small daughter, Birgit, Käthe boarded a train that would take her to Nuremberg, while Wilhelm headed for Berlin. Late in the night, in an East Berlin station, Wilhelm waited with growing concern for his parents to come with the baby, Harald. He searched for them at a second station. In desperation he boarded a subway train that ran below West Berlin. In the last station, at the end of the platform, he saw a couple with a baby carriage.

"It was Uncle Harald!" shout the children.

Eight weeks later, Wilhelm and Käthe began their new life in W. Germany. Near the city of Stuttgart, Wilhelm found work with IBM, an American company, and it was there, while studying English, that he met his friends John and Mary Lanier. At Christmas in 1963, the families exchanged invitations. Wilhelm welcomed the American couple into his home for a German Christmas. The children are pointing gleefully now to a lovely wooden music box that stands in the corner of the room. This music box from the Erzgebirge, with a beautifully carved Nativity Scene revolving slowly on its top, is very important to our story, because this is where Käthe Wohlfahrt's truly begins. The moment the Laniers saw this music box they fell in love with it. What a perfect gift, Wilhelm thought, for these friends who had shown his family such kindness.

"But all of the special Christmas gifts were already gone from the stores!" say the children.

𝒜nd so they were. For in Germany, traditional crafts from the Erzgebirge could only be found during Advent at the outdoor Christmas markets. For two months, Wilhelm searched in vain. Then at last, packed away in a merchant's storeroom, he found an identical music box. But the merchant was in the wholesale business.

"So, Grandpa had to buy ten!" say the children.

The Laniers were thrilled when they saw their gift, and when they learned of the other nine boxes were sure their neighbors would want one too. Mary proposed that they knock on doors in their military apartment building and offer the other boxes for sale. In no time at all, six boxes were gone.

"But then came the Military Police," say the children. "And they took Grandpa Wohlfahrt off to the station!"

And indeed they did. Because, they explained, such door-to-door sales were illegal. But when the Police heard Wilhelm's story, and saw the remaining music boxes, they suggested that he might sell the boxes at the Officers' Wives Club bazaar.

Not only did Wilhelm sell the last boxes, he found himself taking orders for more. Soon Wilhelm and Käthe were spending their weekends selling traditional Erzgebirge crafts at the charity bazaars. Now they needed a name for their company, so they called it…

"Käthe Wohlfahrt's, after Grandma," say the children.

Page 10, upper left:
Rising more than 16 feet, this model of a traditional Erzgebirge Christmas pyramid revolves in Käthe Wohlfahrt's Christmas Village.

Page 10, lower left:
Only a few of the thousands of blown glass ornaments available at Käthe Wohlfahrt's Christmas Village.

Page 11, upper left:
Father Christmas in his traditional robe.

Page 11, lower right:
Modern wax angel typifies traditional models.

What began as a simple gift for a friend had quickly turned into a full-time business! Bus after bus of American soldiers came year round to the Wohlfahrt's home to buy Christmas gifts and decorations. When the family's home in Herrenberg became too small for their growing business, the Wohlfahrt's decided the time had come to move their family once more. They chose the lovely medieval town of Rothenburg ob der Tauber. There, near the famous Market Square, they were able to buy a fine old building that once had housed the city's bakeries.

In the spring of 1977, Käthe Wohlfahrt's Christkindlmarkt opened its doors for year-round business. It was very successful, and two years later a second shop opened on a street nearby.

But the children are saying that now it is time to take you to the Christmas Village!

The Christmas Village

Right in the heart of the Christmas Village, a great white tree sparkles with glass and string upon string of bright little lights, and the stalls in the bustling market place overflow with miniature angels and bells and stars and wooden toys. Above half-timbered houses and snow-covered roofs, thousands of stars glitter and twinkle and shine through the evergreen branches. Little shops beckon the visitor in with shelves of smokers and music boxes, creches and angels and pyramids, ornaments made of the finest blown glass or pewter or brass or wax. Nutcracker Kings are standing on guard, and dolls and bears of every description offer a merry welcome to all who come to the Christmas Village.

A Tradition to Keep

The Käthe Wohlfahrt Christmas shops and Christmas markets represent much more than a business to Wilhelm and Käthe Wohlfahrt. They are a bridge that links a land and people they loved to a new life.

In a world where change comes quickly, and often unexpectedly, families must sometimes choose to leave their town, their country, their way of life, not because they wish to, but because external forces compel them to do so. They carry with them memories of a time and place that was peopled with family, and friends, and rich traditions. They adapt to new customs, to a new generation, but they do not forget the old. And in the old they find something of value, an expression of life which they would like to pass on to their own children. Today, in countries all over the world, Christmas – as it was in the past – is a family celebration. It is perhaps the only day of the year when families, so often scattered today, are able to be together.

In a time of constant change and disposable merchandise and shifting fashions, a time when the future is always a moment away, Christmas remains a time of tradition, when an angel or a nutcracker, a manger scene, or a small glass star is unwrapped with infinite care and pleasure and placed in its old, familiar spot.

In the Erzgebirge, village life was given expression in the wood carvings of the craftsmen. At Christmas their greatest skill and vision, reverence and a sense of wonder, the profound meaning of a candle's light, all of these things were realized in the art of the Christmas pyramid. Into the smokers and nutcrackers went the warmth and congeniality of families and friends gathered together to indulge a story on a winter night.

It is a source of deep pleasure and true satisfaction to Wilhelm and Käthe Wohlfahrt that they are now able to share their love for these Christmas traditions with others and through their stores allow hundreds of craftsmen from Seiffen and Nuremberg and the Tyrolean Alps to reach out across the years and the miles and say with people throughout the world:

Fröhliche Weihnachten!

Merry Christmas!

Page 14, upper right:
The towering nutcracker king, Christian I, stands guard at the Christmas Village in Rothenburg ob der Tauber.

Page 14, lower left:
Mounted nutcracker soldier.

Page 15, right:
Handcarved Christmas pyramid on display in Käthe Wohlfahrt's Christkindlmarkt.

Think of
a little village high in Bavaria's Alps.
A fall of new snow lies white and
clean on village roofs and bridges
and streets. A dark forest of evergreens rises above the valley.

It is early morning in mid-December.
Smoke drifts out of a dozen chimneys,
and a peal of bells announces the
hour, then rolls away through the
valley of small farms, and spruce, and
frozen streams, toward the soaring
spire of a distant church. Now,
the village square comes to life
beneath the tall clock. An old man
arrives and carefully eyes the row of
newly cut Christmas trees. Across
the square, a farm wife lays out her
plates of homemade marzipan, and
greets her neighbor and admires
her display of stars and little straw
angels. Like their mothers and their
grandmothers before them, on this
morning they will exchange the year's
news and talk of life in their
narrow valley.

Or, think of the horn-blowing,
rushing streets of the great city
of Frankfurt am Main.

Darkness has fallen this December
night over office towers and the stock
exchange. Now the dazzling lights
of the Christmas Market draw the
people of the city in. Row after row
of light-strung stalls sell toys and
nutcrackers, gold and glass, creches
and angels and St. Nicholas,
and a thousand other selections.

It is Christmas time in Germany –
as old as the story of
Bethlehem and as new as this
morning's snow.

Christmas in Germany

Cookies and Candles

It is said that nowhere else in the world is the Christmas season longer or celebrated with more enthusiasm than here in Germany. It begins with Advent, when the evergreen wreath is set on the table or hung from the ceiling and four red candles are placed among the branches of spruce or fir or pine. On the fourth Sunday before Christmas, the family gathers around the wreath while Papa or Mama lights the first candle and everyone sings "O Tannenbaum", or "From Heaven High", or "Silent Night." On each successive Sunday another candle will be lit.

For the children there is the calendar with its 24 windows shuttered tight. One by one, day after numbered day, the little windows open to reveal their pictures, or for those who are lucky, a piece of chocolate candy.

Silent Night, Holy Night! All is calm, all is bright 'round yon Virgin mother and child. Holy Infant so tender and mild sleep in heavenly peace, sleep in heavenly peace.

Lithograph of Angel and St. Nicholas dating from 1870–1880.

Child of today in conversation with St. Nicholas.

18

Post cards depict typical Christmas scenes in turn of the century Germany.

On December 4th, St. Barbara's Day, branches of chestnut, cherry, and lilac are cut and placed in a vase of warm salted water. As Christmas approaches the buds open and the vase is filled with a fragrant spray of pink or white or lavender blossoms.

The kitchen rattles with cookie tins and the clinking of spoons and mixing bowls, as it sends out great rolling clouds of ginger and anise and orange-scented air. There are stars and angels and swans to cut out, hearts and trees and flowers to stamp, sugar to sprinkle and almonds and raisins and hazelnuts to stir into the dough. Cookies and cakes and marzipan candies will be heaped on plates in wonderful jumbles by the time Christmas Night arrives.

Children feed edible Christmas tree ornaments to nutcracker in this drawing from the end of the 19th Century.

$\mathcal{N}$ever were two men more closely related than Santa Claus and St. Nicholas. In Germany, for hundreds of years, December 6th has belonged to the Patron Saint of children, St. Nicholas. To him the children give their lists of toys and secret wishes, leaving the list on a window sill or placing it next to a shoe. The list will then be delivered to the Christ Child, who will bring the gifts on Christmas Night.

But St. Nicholas, himself, also carries sweets and small presents for children who have said their prayers. Like Santa Claus, he is said to know just who has been naughty and who has been nice.

As the time before Christmas grows shorter and shorter, people return from mysterious trips to favorite shops and Christmas markets and disappear in a rattle of paper and rib-

German child with traditional Advent Calendar.

bon and swiftly-shut doors. The Christmas creche comes out of the box where it has been stored for so many months and is counted and checked to be sure that no camel has lost his direction, no Wise Man has lost his crown.

Prudent children are careful to leave some hay in their shoes for the Bishop's white horse. In years past, St. Nicholas was accompanied by a frightening knave, who was known as Knight Rupert, and who flourished his rod in a threatening manner and demanded to know if any small boy had been bad.

Brass band plays at Rothenburg ob der Tauber's annual outdoor Christmas market.

Candles are set in their holders as the Christmas pyramid starts to revolve. Nutcracker soldiers line up for inspection, and the smoking man lights his hypnotic pipe.

At last, at last it is Christmas Eve. It is time to trim the Christmas tree with candles and cookies and shining glass balls, with stars and tinsel and marzipan fruits, with horns and horses and angel hair. At the top of the tree is the beautiful wax angel of Nuremberg, with her feathered wings and gold-trimmed robe, reflecting the glow of the candle light. Beneath the tree is the Christmas creche, with shepherds and Wise Men all set in place around the Holy Family.

Candles are lit, a bell is rung, and the doors are thrown open to the living room. The moment the children have waited for through all those calendar-counting, cookie-baking, present-wrapping days has arrived, and each child meets it in his or her own way, one with siren-loud squeals of joy, another with awe-struck silence. Carols are sung and presents are unwrapped amidst paper and thank-you's and Christmas cheer and plates piled high with cookies and sweets.

Then into the frosty night they go. The pealing of bells calls the family to church; candles in windows light their way.

Home, once more, there is Christmas Dinner, goose or blue fish. And then, when they can eat no more – no, not even one last cookie – with Christmas ringing in their ears, the children go up to bed.

Christmas in Seiffen

$\mathcal{I}$magine a night in early winter.
It is long ago, in the mountains outside the little town of Seiffen.
The miners emerge from the black shafts, hang their lanterns
overhead, and climb the steep path to the village.
But tonight will be like no other night of the year.
Tonight will be Christmas in the Erzgebirge.
To learn what that means, we could not do better than to
listen in as Wilhelm Wohlfahrt takes out his box of
Christmas traditions and shares them with
his older granddaughters, Tanya and Simone.

In E

When I was a boy, Grandpa says, we had to start getting ready for Christmas before the first snow fell. Out we would go, into the forest, to look for moss for the Christmas creche. Then on the first Sunday of Advent we would take a wreath of evergreen branches and hang it from the ceiling.

"Sometimes we put our wreath on the table," says Simone.

Yes, and that is very nice also. But this one was hung from the ceiling. Every Sunday we gathered round while my own Papa lit the candles – one, and then two, until just before Christmas all four candles were lit. And we all sang carols...

"Did you sing too?"

"Ah, I sang and I even played on the zither! Yes, your Grandpa could play the zither. Maybe you didn't know that!"

Well, about two weeks before Christmas Night, my Papa would bring in a board from the horse-sled and start to build the Christmas creche. Our Christmas creche had a big, long mountain with a railroad track cutting across it. And every year my Papa would add something new. I, your Grandpa, would be very excited, to see what it would be! One

Christmas it was the Three Wise Men, and once it was a shepherd and sheep, and sometimes there was a new car, or even two or three, to add to the railroad train.

"Was the train very long?"

Very long, says Grandpa.

"Did it have a thousand cars?" asks Tanya.

Well, not quite so many as that. And we always had the figure of a miner wearing his black costume that we would put on the window sill.

"Did he have his guardian angel with him?"

Now, aren't you a clever little girl! Yes, he had his white angel beside him. And the light from their candles shone through the window for everybody to see.

Then the day arrived to go to the spruce woods and cut a fine Christmas tree. When I was a big boy of 12 or 13, I would cut the spruce trees and sell them, and then I would have some money to spend! "How much?" Some coins I could put in my pocket. But I'm telling about our Christmas tree now. We would take it home and decorate it with hanging glass balls and angel hair and little wooden figurines.

Above: Wooden soldiers on parade in a home in the Erzgebirge.

Octagonal church built by the miners is visible in the background of this scene from the town of Seiffen.

24

And then we would all go to mass and come back home for an old fashioned Christmas dinner, my Mama always made nine dishes. There was soup and roast goose that was served with green dumplings… Let's see, how many is that?   "Three." Red cabbage, sauerkraut, bacon-sausage, bread, millet, and a compote of fruit. And then when dinner was over with and the house was very, very quiet… BANG! (Grandpa raps on the table top.) Then, Knight Rupert knocked at the door, dressed in his robe, with his great long list, and one by one he would point to the children and ask if they had been good or bad.   "Had you ever been bad?" Well, maybe once. Maybe just a little bit bad. But never so bad that I didn't get my presents. But I had to recite a verse or a prayer first, before Knight Rupert would hand them over. What would you do if you had to say a verse before you could have your presents?   "I would say it."   "Not me!" Not even a short one? "No!" The little girl shakes her head. Then we read our new books and enjoyed our presents, and I played my zither while the family gathered   around the shining Christmas tree, and   we sang the old Christmas carols until   we had sung every one that we knew.   And we gave the dog an extra sausage,   because Christmas was a magic night   when even the animals talked, it was said.

"Did you ever hear the animals talk?" No. But who knows what they may have said when no one was there to hear them. And it was said that whatever you dreamed on the 12 nights before Epiphany would have a special meaning for the 12 months of the coming year. The first dream would be for January, the second dream for February. And so, at the end of a long, happy day, I said my prayers and climbed into my bed and then I went fast asleep.

Above:
Husband and wife at work in the Erzgebirge early in the 20th Century.

Middle and left:
Wooden rings are turned on a lathe, then sliced into pieces from which the individual animals are carved.

Page 24, lower right and Page 25 lower left:
Early carved Angel and Miner pair in typical costume.

The Pyramid

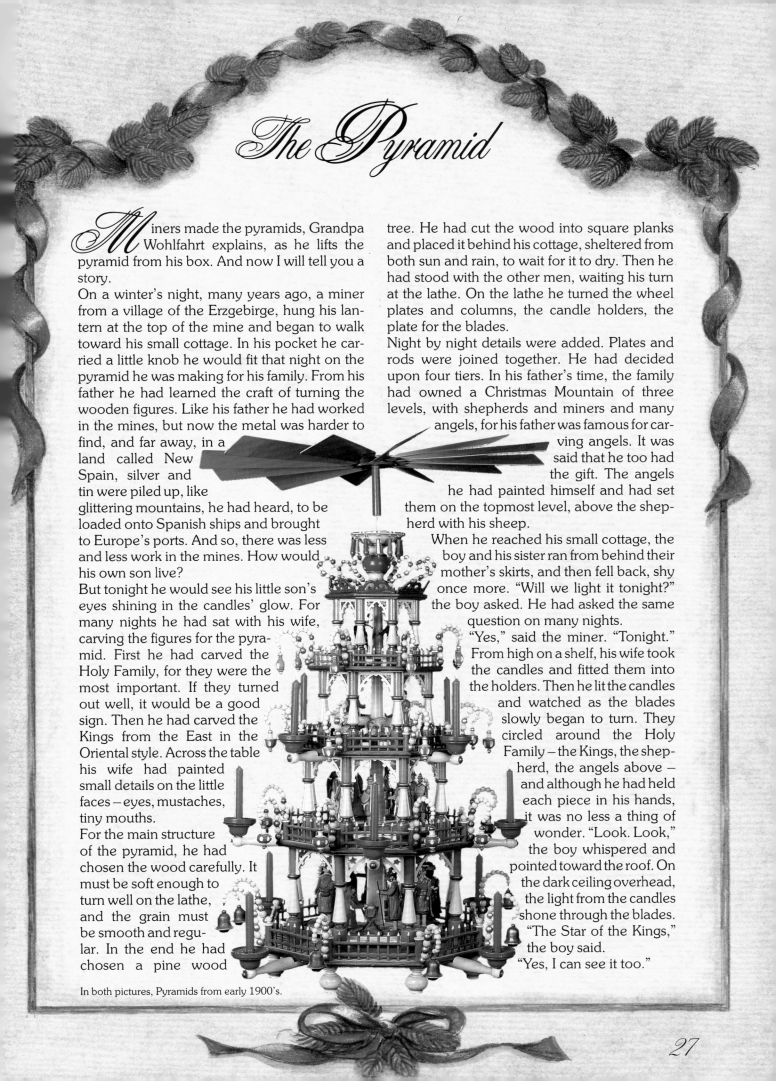

Miners made the pyramids, Grandpa Wohlfahrt explains, as he lifts the pyramid from his box. And now I will tell you a story.

On a winter's night, many years ago, a miner from a village of the Erzgebirge, hung his lantern at the top of the mine and began to walk toward his small cottage. In his pocket he carried a little knob he would fit that night on the pyramid he was making for his family. From his father he had learned the craft of turning the wooden figures. Like his father he had worked in the mines, but now the metal was harder to find, and far away, in a land called New Spain, silver and tin were piled up, like glittering mountains, he had heard, to be loaded onto Spanish ships and brought to Europe's ports. And so, there was less and less work in the mines. How would his own son live?

But tonight he would see his little son's eyes shining in the candles' glow. For many nights he had sat with his wife, carving the figures for the pyramid. First he had carved the Holy Family, for they were the most important. If they turned out well, it would be a good sign. Then he had carved the Kings from the East in the Oriental style. Across the table his wife had painted small details on the little faces – eyes, mustaches, tiny mouths.

For the main structure of the pyramid, he had chosen the wood carefully. It must be soft enough to turn well on the lathe, and the grain must be smooth and regular. In the end he had chosen a pine wood

tree. He had cut the wood into square planks and placed it behind his cottage, sheltered from both sun and rain, to wait for it to dry. Then he had stood with the other men, waiting his turn at the lathe. On the lathe he turned the wheel plates and columns, the candle holders, the plate for the blades.

Night by night details were added. Plates and rods were joined together. He had decided upon four tiers. In his father's time, the family had owned a Christmas Mountain of three levels, with shepherds and miners and many angels, for his father was famous for carving angels. It was said that he too had the gift. The angels he had painted himself and had set them on the topmost level, above the shepherd with his sheep.

When he reached his small cottage, the boy and his sister ran from behind their mother's skirts, and then fell back, shy once more. "Will we light it tonight?" the boy asked. He had asked the same question on many nights.

"Yes," said the miner. "Tonight." From high on a shelf, his wife took the candles and fitted them into the holders. Then he lit the candles and watched as the blades slowly began to turn. They circled around the Holy Family – the Kings, the shepherd, the angels above – and although he had held each piece in his hands, it was no less a thing of wonder. "Look. Look," the boy whispered and pointed toward the roof. On the dark ceiling overhead, the light from the candles shone through the blades. "The Star of the Kings," the boy said.

"Yes, I can see it too."

In both pictures, Pyramids from early 1900's.

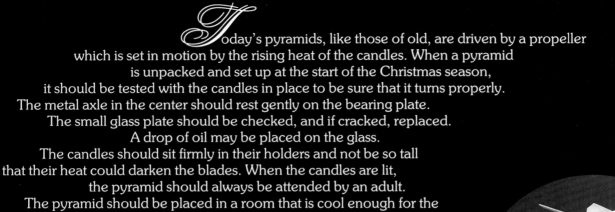

*T*oday's pyramids, like those of old, are driven by a propeller which is set in motion by the rising heat of the candles. When a pyramid is unpacked and set up at the start of the Christmas season, it should be tested with the candles in place to be sure that it turns properly. The metal axle in the center should rest gently on the bearing plate. The small glass plate should be checked, and if cracked, replaced. A drop of oil may be placed on the glass. The candles should sit firmly in their holders and not be so tall that their heat could darken the blades. When the candles are lit, the pyramid should always be attended by an adult. The pyramid should be placed in a room that is cool enough for the air to rise, and away from any drafts. When the candles are lit the blades should start to turn immediately.

1

2

3

Pyramids for Today

5

4

6

1

2

3

4

3. ADVENT

4. ADVENT

2. ADVENT

5

6

7

8

9

About Nutcrackers

Why do some nutcrackers get to be famous? Now, that is a good question, says Grandpa Wohlfahrt. We know that every nutcracker is made in exactly the same way, yet each has his own temperament, and it's true that some do become very famous, like the Nutcracker given to little Marie in "The Nutcracker and the Mouse King." In fact, he was very, very famous and appeared in Mr. Hoffmann's story and Mr. Tschaikowski's ballet. And then there was King Nutcracker in "The Nutcracker and Poor Reinhold," and today our own Christian is starting to make a name for himself. But it wasn't always so. Oh, no! There was a time in the Erzgebirge when nutcrackers were completely unknown. Families then would struggle and strain to crack their walnuts and hazelnuts, pounding away with hammers and fists, while the grandpas tried to tell their stories. And then at last, some very smart person – and I suspect that it was a grandpa – fashioned a pair of wooden tongs for people to use to crack their walnuts. But these early nutcrackers had no shape, and not one was ever the least bit famous.

Then more years passed, and another grandpa, who happened to be a woodcarver too, dressed his nutcracker up like a soldier and gave him a fine pair of wooden boots so that he could stand at attention. And then he said to him, "Get to work!" And a neighbor who had been ordered that day to do this and do that and come here and go there by a soldier in the village, said, "Ha! Now there's a fine thing to have!" And before you know it, every villager wanted a nutcracker soldier to order about. And that is why nutcrackers had to be dressed in uniforms back then. Only people who wielded a lot of authority could be the models for nutcrackers. And perhaps this is where the nutcrackers got the notion that they could be famous.

Above: "After the day's work."

But why does one become more famous than another? We still haven't answered that. Every nutcracker – famous or not – begins as a plank of wood. He may be spruce or he may be beech or he may be alder or pine. Now he must wait for at least six months, while his timber is being cured. Then he is cut into a square and is put in a room to dry. From the very beginning nutcrackers have to learn to be very patient. Next, the basic form of his body and his other parts are turned on a lathe. Then back to another dry room he goes for a second curing period. When all the parts are ready and dry, holes are drilled for dowel connections. Then he is milled and cut and polished, and only at the very last is he issued his boots and uniform. By then, he has always grown a beard and his hair has gotten nice and long, and he may have grown a mustache. Buttons and braid are painted on, belts and swords are issued to some, and then the most important moment of all in a nutcracker's life takes place: he is given his fine set of teeth. And these he wears proudly all his life – and a nutcracker's life is very long. Now, every nutcracker, large or small, is strong and proud and patient, too. So you see, it may be, when the time is right, and given a chance, any nutcracker you encounter may one day go on to become very famous.

Early nutcrackers stand at attention.

*A*lthough modern nutcrackers are usually assigned to stand guard
and provide decoration, they – like their predecessors, large and small –
have been trained to crack a walnut or hazelnut when called upon to do so.
Among the troops well represented are Cavalry and Infantry, Hussars and Sovereign Soldiers,
and of course, the Nutcracker Kings.
In addition, policemen and tradesmen have come from the villages of the Erzgebirge.
Large or small, soldier or King, each stands ready to serve.

Royal Guards

8

9

10

11

12

13

8

9

10

11

12

13

14

The Jovial Turk

Now, the Jovial Turk will make our living room smell like Christmas, says Grandpa Wohlfahrt, as he sets up the little turbaned smoker on the table beside him. Soon a slowly curling ribbon of smoke appears from the smoker's dark mouth and the pungent aroma of forest air drifts through the living room. Even Grandpa, himself, seems hypnotized by the atmosphere of the smoker.

Years ago, he begins to explain, incense was burned in the church on special occasions. You may remember that the Three Kings brought a gift of frankincense to the Holy Infant. In the Erzgebirge incense was made from charcoal, sawdust, and potato starch and then was soaked with perfumed water to give it a pleasant aroma when it was burned. Lavender, jasmine, cinnamon, myrrh – all of these were familiar scents. At Christmas time, the people would set their incense on a piece of clay, and that was the way they enjoyed the scented smoke.

But how did the incense get inside the Turk? That story belongs to Ferdinand Froh and his nephew Gotthelf Haustein. These gentlemen lived in Saxony, long ago, in the 1800's, when smoking a pipe was something new for men of the Erzgebirge. You see, up until then it was only the men who came from the land of the Turks who smoked their long meerschaum pipes. Good Christian men were not allowed to indulge in smoking pipes. Of course, a few Foresters were known to go deep into the forest and light a pipe from time to time. But in 1850, times were changing, and modern men were permitted to smoke their pipes outdoors and in public houses.

So, Mr. Froh and Mr. Haustein, sat in a public house one evening, drinking and talking as gentlemen did then, and watched their companions smoke their pipes. And they thought to themselves, "What an excellent thing, to sit with good friends in a warm, cozy room and watch the smoke curling out of the pipes!"

Now, had they come from another place, the story might well have ended there. But these were men from the Erzgebirge, where people knew how to make wooden figures. "What if I carved a wooden man and could make the smoke come out of his mouth like that gentleman's over there?" said Mr. Ferdinand Froh. "That's a fine idea!" said Mr. Haustein. "But how could we get such a thing to work?"

Well, they looked at the smoke and thought of the incense pellets they burned at Christmas time. If they could put their wooden figures and the incense pellets together somehow...

You can see with our Turk how they did it. First they hollowed the figure out. Then they set a plate on the legs. They drilled holes so the smoker could draw in fresh air and a fine round mouth for the smoke to come out. And that is how it has come to be, that we sit here in our own warm room, enjoying each other's company, while our Jovial Turk smokes his pipe.

Early smoking men include Turks, policemen, and miners.

From the Jovial Turk and the Forester, the family of smoking men
has grown to include many other members. Both Father Christmas
and Santa Claus, rambling dwarves and St. Peter himself, Wise Men, merchants,
smithies and peddlers, men from the village and men from the farms,
all now smoke their pipes. In addition to the traditional scents of lavender and myrrh,
new fragrances are available: Christmas Fragrance, Forest Air, Alpine Herbs,
Sandalwood and many, many more. Incense cones should be stored in normal humidity.
Just as in the earliest days of the smoker, the cone is placed
on an upright base that sits on top of the smoker's legs.
The incense is lit and then blown out.
Then the smoker's body is set back in place,
and he is ready to enjoy his pipe.

Smoking Men

8

9

10

11

1

2

3

5

6

7

The Music Box

Of course, every sort of person may be put on top of a music box when it comes from the Erzgebirge, says Grandpa Wohlfahrt. Not just miners and angels and shepherds and figures from the Nativity Story. Yes, even children and grandpas are welcome to take a turn on a music box. Certainly, dogs and cats, as well – he assures his little grand-daughters – as long as they are well be-haved.

Have you ever seen a Noah's Ark, with the animals lined up two by two, or they may have been kept together on a ring? Or, have you seen a little carved farm, with the farmer's family and chickens and cows and horses and goats and pigs? The woodcarvers of the Erzgebirge have always had a special gift for carving scenes from everyday life, as well as carving the Bethlehem story. I have seen a box with a young girl feeding grain to her hungry geese, and a box where the game warden chases a poacher, and a box where young couples dance to music around a St. John's tree. And one that I like very much, a Kurrende scene, where carolers sing as they carry their star in front of the eight-sided church that the miners built in the village of Seiffen.

If you were carving a box of your own, what would you put on the top? Grandpa asks. The Baby Jesus in the manger. Yes, that would be a very good thing. And Mary and Joseph, and a cow and six sheep. And a shepherd to keep the sheep together. Yes. And the Three Kings with their camels to ride. And their gifts. No, you shouldn't forget the gifts. And an angel and St. Nicholas. And more presents. Yes, that would be very good. And a Christmas tree – the kind that has candles. And another angel. And Grandpa and Grandma. Ah, you are very nice children! And Auntie Carmen. And Papa and

Mama. And the little gray cat that lives next door. And baby Kenta and little Aska. And Tanya's teacher. And an elephant like you saw at the zoo. And a bear. And a duck. And a swan. And a dog. Yes, this will be a very fine box, indeed.

Should we have your music box play a song or should it be silent as it. turns around? Yes, I see, it has to play a song or it wouldn't be a music box. But there was a time long ago when you wound the spring on the bottom of the box, and it went round and round without ever making a sound. And then someone put a metal strip into the wooden box. As the box went round and round, a peg would hit the strip, and "Plink!" it would go. "Plink. Plink. Plink." People called it a jingle box. Then the Swiss, who already knew about making clock-work, designed a metal cylin-der with pins and a comb, and the boxes played beautiful music. So, what song shall we have your music box play? " Silent Night ? " Can that many people and ani-mals turn around very quietly? No, that might be very hard... Simone suggests " O Tannenbaum." Yes, that will be just the right melody.

Above: "Next to the jingle box."
Craftsmen at work assembling music boxes.

Early carousel.

Our modern music boxes show a variety of figures and scenes, from carolers circling the Seiffen church to Father Christmas at a Christmas tree to the Holy Family of Bethlehem. Among the songs that the boxes play are "Silent Night," "O Tannenbaum," and "O Ye Merry Christmastime." To hear the music and watch the scene as the little carved figures turn, one has only to wind the spring on the bottom and pull the wooden peg on the side, and the music box will work its charm.

1

3

2

Carousels

4

5

To the miners of the Erzgebirge, light was a rare and beautiful gift. From the unending blackness of the mines where they labored and the darkness of the long winter nights, the light of a candle brought hope and warmth, a reminder of the world overhead, and a signal, when hung at the top of the mine, that the men were up safely for another day. Thus, the angel who stood at the miner's side to guard him through his dark days and nights always carried a light.

1

2

3

4

5

Candelabra

Oh, Christmas Tree

Remember a Christmas Day now past. Can you see the family Christmas tree with its string of lights that blinked — or did not — and the painted balls that hung from the branches?

Perhaps there was one glass ornament that held a special fascination — the shape, the color, a spiral of glitter, some detail that caused your eyes to return.

Were there snaking strings of silver tinsel, or beads, or old-fashioned popcorn and cranberry chains? Were narrow strands of silver icicles thrown at the tree in abandoned handfuls or carefully draped, one strand at a time, on the needled tips of the branches? Or, perhaps the tree was finished with angel hair?

And the top. Was it a star or an angel or something else or nothing at all? Were presents under the tree for days, or did they appear on Christmas Eve or even on Christmas morning? Was the tree so tall you could not reach the top?

How vivid our memories often are.

The Christmas tree, whether indoors or out, green or white or some wild, bright color, with lights or candles, and decorations that are simple or artfully intricate, has become the center of much of our Christmas celebration today.

Like so many other Christmas traditions, it began in Germany.

There is a charming legend — alas, untrue — that Martin Luther returning home through the forest on a dark clear night was struck by the beauty of the stars overhead as they glittered through the evergreen branches. Out of this vision came the idea to place lighted candles on a tree.

To whom belongs the honor of adding candlelight to the Christmas tree is something that we, today, may never know. Yet, the truth may not be so different from the legend.

For, candles, like stars, have always been beacons that lure us through the dark night.

Evergreens, since time out of memory, have represented hope and the promise that nature will renew each year.

Forest

In medieval times the evergreen was said to be the Tree of Knowledge. On its branches were hung apples as a symbol of Man's fall from grace and communion wafers to represent his salvation. But the Christmas tree as we know it today took form during the time of the Reformation in northern Europe. In the city of Strasbourg in 1605, a visitor was impressed to see in a family parlor a fir tree which was decorated with paper roses, apples, wafers, gold foil, and sweets. So popular did such trees become in central and northern Germany, that fiery Protestant ministers soon began to warn against these vanities. In wealthier homes it was common for each family member to have a tree of his or her own.

At that time, a separate tradition, the Christmas pyramid, claimed a prominent place in homes in eastern regions of Germany, particularly in Saxony and in Berlin. It was on the pyramid that one found candles and a star at the top to welcome the Christ Child and light the way for his visit. Indeed, the Christmas tree as we know it today, with its combination of lights and decorations, may be the result of the fusion of these two different Christmas customs.

It was during the 1800's that the Christmas tree with its decorations began to spread over much of Europe and across the Atlantic Ocean as well. Often a royal marriage brought the Christmas tree to a new land. In Austria and Bavaria, brides insisted on their Christmas trees, and in England, Queen Victoria's consort, Albert, brought a tree into the palace.

When in 1848 the "Illustrated London News" ran a picture of the Royal Family gathered around their Christmas tree, the English Christmas was changed forever. At the same time, German immigrants carried their love of the Christmas tree with them to their new homes in America. Soon the toymakers of Nuremberg, the glassblowers of Lauscha, the woodcarvers of the Erzgebirge, and the craftsmen of dozens of Alpine villages found themselves hard-worked to keep up with the new demand for ornaments. In a few short years, the Christmas tree had assumed a role of undisputed prominence. Few can imagine Christmas today without the Christmas tree.

There are extraordinary stories in the history of the Christmas tree. In 1914, German soldiers came over the trenches on Christmas Eve with trees for their British counterparts. But perhaps this story from World War I is not so unusual after all. There has always been something magical about the Christmas tree.

Above and lower right: Christmas trees decorated with sweets in German homes during the first half of the 19th Century.

Throughout
the year the toymakers of Germany
and the woodcarvers of the Erzgebirge
used their craft and impressive skill
to fashion beautiful toys and figures
for the families of other men.
But at Christmas time, with the small
bits of wood and paint left from
larger pieces, they created tiny horses
and trains, sleds and soldiers
to delight their own children.
In central and southern Germany,
flat pieces were cut with a saw,
in the Erzgebirge the miniature figures,
like the larger ones,
were turned on a lathe.
The marvelous ornaments seen on
today's Christmas tree were
produced in West Germany.
They reflect the different traditions of
woodcrafts that exist in Germany.

Ornaments of Wood

Ornaments of Glass

*A*s long ago
as the 1500's, the glass bead makers of Lauscha
blew large glass balls for their own homes.
As the years passed, and the markets for beads
began to dwindle away, they discovered
that they were able to sell their big "kugels".
Then, in 1857, a Lauscha glassblower,
Louis Greiner-Schlotfeger, discovered the
formula then being used to silver the inside of
glass. A cast was made from a wooden mold,
the heated glass was poured into the cast,
and the ornament was blown.
The silver solution was poured inside,
shaken round, then the ball was dried, dyed,
and lacquered, and given its final details
and a hanger. From the simple ball of long ago
come the often complex shapes and designs
that are seen in Lauscha ornaments today.

Ornaments of Pewter

The toymakers of Nuremberg were famous for their tin and pewter toys. Like craftsmen throughout Germany, they turned their skill at Christmas time to the making of Christmas ornaments.

The first pewter ornaments were made 200 years ago and were shaped like little drops and bowls to reflect the candlelight. Later, pieces of colored glass were added to the ornaments.

The intricacy of the shapes today is a beautiful thing to behold, and a tribute to the tradition of tin and pewter figures which was developed in Nuremberg. Familiar figures now include St. Nicholas, Mary and the Infant, and the decorated Christmas tree, but the best known figure is that of the Angel sounding the joy of Christmas.

Away in a Manger

First came the Master Singer bearing a great star on a pole. Next came a village tradesman holding high a Christmas tree decked with ribbons and apples. Behind, the various actors followed, the shepherds and angels and innkeepers, the young girl who would represent Mary and the merchant who had been named to play Joseph, then three men dressed in the style of the Orient Kings and the one who would play the villain, Herod. All marched in solemn procession, through the village, to the church, singing the old carols.

In villages all over Germany, in churches and halls and village squares, beginning on the first Advent Sunday, the Christmas Story was played. Using the dialect of the region, the villagers re-enacted the Nativity. Often they added small, homely details that reflected their own lives: "Three eggs and some butter we bring too," announced a sincere shepherd. "A fowl to make some broth if thy Mother can cook it – put some dripping in and 'twill be good. Because we've nothing else – we are but poor shepherds – accept our good will."

St. Francis of Assisi would have been pleased by such Christmas pageants and by the creche scenes he might see today in churches and homes and market squares. But in 1223, St. Francis was troubled. He looked at the faces of the people who came to worship at his church in Greccio. They were good people, and he wanted to teach them the true meaning of Christmas. The story was told in the Holy Scriptures, but only churchmen and scholars could read; and the Mass was given in Latin, not in the everyday language that was spoken by his flock. Still, he knew, he must find a way to make the Bethlehem story real and accessible to these people he loved.

After first obtaining permission from the Supreme Pontiff of the Church, St. Francis set about preparing an extraordinary Christmas service. On Christmas Eve, he gave to his flock the first living Nativity Scene. Men, women, and children arrived for worship at the church in Greccio to find a manger filled with fresh hay. There by the manger were Mary and Joseph, played by living people. Shepherds worshipped a life-sized wax Infant; and not just shepherds, but a live ox and a donkey stood beside the manger. Then St. Francis, himself, told the people the Story, and together they sang the holy songs.

The impact of this manger scene was immediate and profound; nor has it lessened in the nearly 800 years since St. Francis first conceived it. The Nativity Story was staged in Greccio the next Christmas and on every Christmas that followed. The custom spread, with each year that passed, further and further from the town where it started. The Nativity Scene took a new name in every country it entered: in Italy it was called a "presepe", in France a "crèche", in Spain the "nacimiento", and in Germany, the Christmas "Krippe", or crib. But everywhere, the story it told was the same. Near the end of the Middle Ages, the Nativity Scene was carved from wood, or molded out of clay or wax, and set up first in churches, but soon in private homes and public buildings as well. Noblemen often vied with each other to set up elaborate Bethlehem scenes. In most homes, however, the Christmas creche was built gradually, a figure or two at a time over several years, and was passed down to the next generation.

In the Erzgebirge, three-tiered creches were carved. Known as Christmas Mountains, they included, on the central level, the Holy Family surrounded by the figures of the shepherds and Kings. A variety of carved animals were often included in the manger scene. On the uppermost level appeared the angels. And below – as in life they worked below ground – were the figures of the miners themselves, along with their traditional guardian angels.

Today, the largest Nativity Scene can be found in Rome, and the finest collection of German cribs may be seen in Munich in the Bayerisches National Museum. But the best-loved creches are often found on a table top or under the Tree in homes throughout the world.

This Nativity scene was carved in the Alps around 1930.

The spectacular creche shown below is the product of nearly 400 years of craftsmanship that has passed from generation to generation in the isolated valley of Gröden, high in the South Tyrolean Alps. In this tiny valley, cut off throughout the long winter by impassable mountain walls, the carving of wood has become not just a way of life but has reached the level of art. Long known throughout Europe for the quality of their carving, the craftsmen of Gröden were united in 1912 by Anton Riffeser. From his vision came the House of ANRI, whose artisans created this modern creche. Carved of fine Alpine maple wood and painted by hand, each figure stands on a wooden base for individual placement.

The First Noël

The Angel of Nuremberg

It is said that in the time of the Thirty Years War, there lived a man in Nuremberg by the name of Balthasar Hauser. A doll maker, he lived with his wife and together they worked to create their dolls. He would carve, and his wife and their little daughter would paint the faces.

These were dark years in Germany, when armies moved across the land and the roads were filled with refugees. So Balthasar Hauser thanked the Lord for his good wife and the sweet child and the work he had found for his hands to do. And so life went on, until one day when the little girl was taken ill. No longer could she sit at the table painting the dolls along with her mother. Balthasar Hauser worked with his knife, but his fingers seemed to have lost their way. And then his wife called him to come quickly to where the little one lay in her bed.

"I have seen the angel," the little girl said, her eyes bright with the fever and yet with peace in them too. "Just now, while I slept." And though his wife tried to quiet the child to save the little strength she had, the little girl would go on. "She had wings and a crown and gold in her robe, and her face was filled with joy and peace, and she came to me and she smiled."

Two days passed and the little one died, and almost as great to bear as the loss of the child was the grief that he saw in her mother's face. He took up a block of wood and a knife, and then he began to carve. And now his fingers sped for he knew so well the features of the doll he carved.

He dressed her in a robe of gold and fashioned the wings from feathers. And then he gave her to his wife, and she gasped when she saw the beautiful doll and tears came into her eyes.

"It's our little one," she said quietly.

Today's angels, made of wax, still bear the lovely features of the little girl of Nuremberg.

1

2

3

4

5

A Christmas Dinner

Can you taste
the turkey and cranberry sauce and
smell the pumpkin pie? Let us join a
family in Germany and share
their Christmas dinner.

We return from church through
the chilly darkness, hurrying down
the narrow street toward home.

Then, pulling off our coats,
we arrive to find the house filled with
the smells of goose and Christmas
sausage and ablaze with the
light of candles.

The table is set with the finest linen
napkins and a beautiful lace table
cloth. It comes from Annaberg, we are
told, and has been in the family
for a hundred years.
Evergreen branches and ribbon and
candles add a special holiday mood.

Our places are laid with china and
crystal, and by each plate we find a tiny
wooden angel holding a candle.
As our glasses are filled, the dishes
begin to arrive: dumplings and sausage
and two kinds of cabbage,
herring salad and a dish of baked
apples, and in the center the steaming
roast goose, crisp and brown
and stuffed to bursting.

"In my Grandmother's house,
we always had carp,"
our hostess now explains to us,
"but the children prefer a goose."
At the end, there is a plate of cookies,
one for every place, with ginger
cookies and marzipan fruits, honey
cookies, and nuts.

Dinner After

After dinner, a small table is set with a linen table cloth, which is bordered with eyelet and embroidered flowers. It will one day be handed down to the family's young daughter. But for now, a welcome silence descends as friends depart and the children go off to their beds. With a cup of coffee or hot mulled wine, Mama and Papa rest at last and enjoy a moment of quiet reflection. To this Christmas they bring their memories of so many holiday seasons shared, and they take away moments, both sweet and funny, that will always recall this day. Amidst candles and flowers and evergreen branches, Christmas evening now comes to an end. It is time to say Good Night.

All objects presented here may be obtained from Käthe Wohlfahrt's *(see price list)*

Christmas in Rothenburg

We return now
to where our journey began, to Rothenburg ob der Tauber.
Let us join in as this medieval town celebrates another Christmas season.
The red roofs are now white with snow and a frost-filled haze hangs over
the Tauber Valley. On the final days of November, the Market Square
comes to bustling life with the opening of its annual Christmas
market, the Reiterlesmarkt. There, below the Town Hall and Ratstrink-
stube, in the shadow of St. Jacob's Church, canopied stalls offer stars
and toys, a world of Christmas ornaments and traditional crafts and
decorations, cookies and cakes and candles and evergreens. The Market
spills out to the Herrngasse and into the Town Hall's inner courtyard,
filling the center of Rothenburg with a maze of sparkling stands.
In almost every German city and town, we will find a Christmas Market,
and each has its own atmosphere, with local foods and handicrafts on
display in the town square. In Rothenburg, we may leave the market and
take a carriage ride through the town, the clatter of the horses'
hooves ringing out on the cobbled streets, as we look at the town's
decorations and view the solemn Nativity Scene. Then we return to the
Market Square to warm ourselves with a hot spiced drink,
known in Germany as "Glühwein." There are special traditions in
Rothenburg. At night, we hear the call of the Night Watchman sounding
across the roof tops. And in early December, the children march
through the streets and into the Market Square in a beautiful candlelight
procession to be greeted by the mayor himself.
There is music to be heard. A brass band plays for visitors
to the Christmas Market, and through the streets, as dusk descends
star singers carry their stars and lanterns, as they sing the old
Christmas carols. In the church there are choir and organ concerts,
and bells that ring out on Advent Sundays.
It is a joyous season in Rothenburg, as it is in every country
and town where Christmas is celebrated.